*Commissioned for the Festival to celebrate the
Consecration of St. Michael's Cathedral, Coventry, May 1962*

BENJAMIN BRITTEN

WAR REQUIEM

op. 66

*"My subject is War, and the pity of War.
The Poetry is in the pity...
All a poet can do today is warn."*
Wilfred Owen

*Words from the Missa pro Defunctis
and the poems of Wilfred Owen*

★

Vocal Score

by Imogen Holst

BOOSEY & HAWKES

Boosey & Hawkes Music Publishers Ltd
www.boosey.com

In loving memory of

Roger Burney,   *Sub-Lieutenant*
Royal Naval Volunteer Reserve

Piers Dunkerley,   *Captain*
Royal Marines

David Gill,   *Ordinary Seaman*
Royal Navy

Michael Halliday,   *Lieutenant*
Royal New Zealand Naval Volunteer Reserve

B. & H. 18940

I. REQUIEM AETERNAM

CHORUS

Requiem aeternam dona eis Domine,
et lux perpetua luceat eis.

BOYS' CHOIR

Te decet hymnus, Deus in Sion;
et tibi reddetur votum in Jerusalem;
exaudi orationem meam, ad te omnis caro veniet.

TENOR SOLO

What passing-bells for these who die as cattle?
    Only the monstrous anger of the guns.
    Only the stuttering rifles' rapid rattle
Can patter out their hasty orisons.
No mockeries for them from prayers or bells,
    Nor any voice of mourning save the choirs,—
The shrill, demented choirs of wailing shells;
    And bugles calling for them from sad shires.

What candles may be held to speed them all?
    Not in the hands of boys, but in their eyes
Shall shine the holy glimmers of good-byes.
    The pallor of girls' brows shall be their pall;
Their flowers the tenderness of silent minds,
And each slow dusk a drawing-down of blinds.

CHORUS

Kyrie eleison, Christe eleison, Kyrie eleison.

II. DIES IRAE

CHORUS

Dies irae, dies illa,
Solvet saeclum in favilla,
Teste David cum Sibylla.

Quantus tremor est futurus,
Quando Judex est venturus,
Cuncta stricte discussurus!

Tuba mirum spargens sonum
Per sepulchra regionum
Coget omnes ante thronum.

Mors stupebit et natura,
Cum resurget creatura,
Judicanti responsura.

BARITONE SOLO

Bugles sang, saddening the evening air,
And bugles answered, sorrowful to hear.

Voices of boys were by the river-side.
Sleep mothered them; and left the twilight sad.
The shadow of the morrow weighed on men.

Voices of old despondency resigned,
Bowed by the shadow of the morrow, slept.

SOPRANO SOLO AND CHORUS

Liber scriptus proferetur,
In quo totum continetur,
Unde mundus judicetur.

Judex ergo cum sedebit,
Quidquid latet, apparebit:
Nil inultum remanebit.

Quid sum miser tunc dicturus?
Quem patronum rogaturus,
Cum vix justus sit securus?

Rex tremendae majestatis,
Qui salvandos salvas gratis,
Salva me, fons pietatis.

B.& H. 18940

Out there, we've walked quite friendly up to Death;
    Sat down and eaten with him, cool and bland,—
Pardoned his spilling mess-tins in our hand.
We've sniffed the green thick odour of his breath,—
Our eyes wept, but our courage didn't writhe.
He's spat at us with bullets and he's coughed
    Shrapnel. We chorussed when he sang aloft;
We whistled while he shaved us with his scythe.

Oh, Death was never enemy of ours!
    We laughed at him, we leagued with him, old chum.
No soldier's paid to kick against his powers.
    We laughed, knowing that better men would come,
And greater wars; when each proud fighter brags
He wars on Death—for Life; not men—for flags.

CHORUS

Recordare Jesu pie,   Qui Mariam absolvisti,
Quod sum causa tuae viae: Et latronem exaudisti,
Ne me perdas illa die.   Mihi quoque spem dedisti.

Quaerens me, sedisti lassus: Inter oves locum praesta,
Redemisti crucem passus: Et ab haedis me sequestra,
Tantus labor non sit cassus.   Statuens in parte dextra.

Ingemisco, tamquam reus: Confutatis maledictis,
Culpa rubet vultus meus: Flammis acribus addictis,
Supplicanti parce Deus.   Voca me cum benedictis.

Oro supplex et acclinis,
Cor contritum quasi cinis:
Gere curam mei finis.

BARITONE SOLO

Be slowly lifted up, thou long black arm,
Great gun towering toward Heaven, about to curse;

Reach at that arrogance which needs thy harm,
And beat it down before its sins grow worse;

But when thy spell be cast complete and whole,
May God curse thee, and cut thee from our soul!

CHORUS AND SOPRANO SOLO

Dies irae, dies illa,   Quantus tremor est futurus,
Solvet saeclum in favilla,   Quando Judex est venturus,
Teste David cum Sibylla.   Cuncta stricte discussurus!

Lacrimosa dies illa,
Qua resurget ex favilla,
Judicandus homo reus,
Huic ergo parce Deus.

TENOR SOLO

Move him into the sun—
Gently its touch awoke him once,
At home, whispering of fields unsown.
Always it woke him, even in France,
Until this morning and this snow.
If anything might rouse him now
The kind old sun will know.

Think how it wakes the seeds,—
Woke, once, the clays of a cold star.
Are limbs, so dear-achieved, are sides,
Full-nerved—still warm—too hard to stir?
Was it for this the clay grew tall?
—O what made fatuous sunbeams toil
To break earth's sleep at all?

CHORUS

Pie Jesu Domine, dona eis requiem. Amen.

B.& H 18940

III. OFFERTORIUM

BOYS' CHOIR

Domine Jesu Christe, Rex gloriae, libera animas omnium fidelium
defunctorum de poenis inferni, et de profondo lacu:
libera eas de ore leonis, ne absorbeat eas tartarus, ne cadant in obscurum.

CHORUS

Sed signifer sanctus Michael repraesentet eas in lucem sanctam:
quam olim Abrahae promisisti, et semini ejus.

BARITONE AND TENOR SOLOS

So Abram rose, and clave the wood, and went,
And took the fire with him, and a knife.
And as they sojourned both of them together,
Isaac the first-born spake and said, My Father,
Behold the preparations, fire and iron,
But where the lamb for this burnt-offering?
Then Abram bound the youth with belts and straps,
And builded parapets and trenches there,
And stretchèd forth the knife to slay his son.
When lo! an angel called him out of heaven,
Saying, Lay not thy hand upon the lad,
Neither do anything to him. Behold,
A ram, caught in a thicket by its horns;
Offer the Ram of Pride instead of him.
But the old man would not so, but slew his son,—
And half the seed of Europe, one by one.

BOYS' CHOIR

Hostias et preces tibi Domine laudis offerimus:
tu suscipe pro animabus illis, quarum hodie memoriam facimus:
fac eas, Domine, de morte transire ad vitam.

IV. SANCTUS

SOPRANO SOLO AND CHORUS

Sanctus, sanctus, sanctus Dominus Deus Sabaoth.
Pleni sunt coeli et terra gloria tua, Hosanna in excelsis.
Benedictus qui venit in nomine Domini. Hosanna in excelsis.

BARITONE SOLO

After the blast of lightning from the East,
The flourish of loud clouds, the Chariot Throne;
After the drums of Time have rolled and ceased,
And by the bronze west long retreat is blown,

Shall life renew these bodies? Of a truth
All death will He annul, all tears assuage?—
Fill the void veins of Life again with youth,
And wash, with an immortal water, Age?

When I do ask white Age he saith not so:
"My head hangs weighed with snow."
And when I hearken to the Earth, she saith:
"My fiery heart shrinks, aching. It is death.
Mine ancient scars shall not be glorified,
Nor my titanic tears, the sea, be dried."

V. AGNUS DEI

TENOR SOLO

One ever hangs where shelled roads part.
In this war He too lost a limb,
But His disciples hide apart;

CHORUS
And now the Soldiers bear with Him.

Agnus Dei, qui tollis peccata mundi, dona eis requiem.

Near Golgotha strolls many a priest,
And in their faces there is pride
That they were flesh-marked by the Beast

CHORUS
By whom the gentle Christ's denied.

Agnus Dei, qui tollis peccata mundi, dona eis requiem.

The scribes on all the people shove
And bawl allegiance to the state,
But they who love the greater love
Lay down their life; they do not hate.

CHORUS

Agnus Dei, qui tollis peccata mundi, dona eis requiem sempiternam.

Dona nobis pacem.

VI. LIBERA ME

CHORUS AND SOPRANO SOLO

Libera me, Domine, de morte aeterna, in die illa tremenda :
Quando coeli movendi sunt et terra : Dum veneris judicare saeculum per ignem.
Tremens factus sum ego, et timeo, dum discussio venerit, atque ventura ira.
Quando coeli movendi sunt et terra. Dies illa, dies irae, calamitatis et miseriae,
dies magna et amara valde. Libera me, Domine . . .

TENOR SOLO

It seemed that out of battle I escaped
Down some profound dull tunnel, long since scooped
Through granites which titanic wars had groined.
Yet also there encumbered sleepers groaned,
Too fast in thought or death to be bestirred.
Then, as I probed them, one sprang up, and stared
With piteous recognition in fixed eyes,
Lifting distressful hands as if to bless.

And no guns thumped, or down the flues made moan.
"Strange friend," I said, "here is no cause to mourn."

BARITONE SOLO

"None," said the other, "save the undone years,
The hopelessness. Whatever hope is yours,
Was my life also; I went hunting wild
After the wildest beauty in the world.

For by my glee might many men have laughed,
And of my weeping something had been left,
Which must die now. I mean the truth untold,
The pity of war, the pity war distilled.
Now men will go content with what we spoiled.
Or, discontent, boil bloody, and be spilled.
They will be swift with swiftness of the tigress,
None will break ranks, though nations trek from progress.
Miss we the march of this retreating world
Into vain citadels that are not walled.
Then, when much blood had clogged their chariot-wheels
I would go up and wash them from sweet wells,
Even from wells we sunk too deep for war,
Even the sweetest wells that ever were.

I am the enemy you killed, my friend.
I knew you in this dark; for so you frowned
Yesterday through me as you jabbed and killed.
I parried ; but my hands were loath and cold."

TENOR AND BARITONE SOLOS

"Let us sleep now . . ."

BOYS' CHOIR, CHORUS AND SOPRANO SOLO

In paradisum deducant te Angeli: in tuo adventu suscipiant te Martyres, et perducant te in civitatem sanctam Jerusalem.
Chorus Angelorum te suscipiat, et cum Lazaro quondam paupere aeternam habeas requiem.
Requiem aeternam dona eis, Domine; et lux perpetua luceat eis.
Requiescant in pace. Amen.

The poems of Wilfred Owen are reprinted by permission of Mr Harold Owen and Chatto & Windus Ltd.

B. & H. 18940

The first performance of WAR REQUIEM *was given in St Michael's Cathedral, Coventry, on 30th May, 1962. The soloists were Heather Harper, Peter Pears and Dietrich Fischer-Dieskau, with the Coventry Festival Chorus, City of Birmingham Symphony Orchestra, Melos Ensemble, and the boys of Holy Trinity, Leamington and Holy Trinity, Stratford. The chorus and full orchestra were conducted by Meredith Davies and the chamber orchestra by the composer.*

VOICES

Soprano, Tenor and Baritone *Solos*

Mixed Chorus

Boys' Choir

ORCHESTRA

3 Flutes
(Fl. III doubling Piccolo)
2 Oboes
English Horn
3 Clarinets
(Cl. III doubling Cl. in E♭ and Bass Cl.)
2 Bassoons
Double bassoon
6 Horns in F
4 Trumpets in C
3 Trombones
Tuba
Pianoforte
Organ
(or Harmonium*)

Timpani
Percussion (4 *players*)
  2 Side Drums
  Tenor Drum
  Bass Drum
  Tambourine
  Triangle
  Cymbals
  Castanets
  Whip
  Chinese Blocks
  Gong
  Bells (C and F♯)
  Vibraphone
  Glockenspiel
  Antique Cymbals (C and F♯)
Strings

CHAMBER ORCHESTRA

Flute (doubling Piccolo), Oboe (doubling English Horn), Clarinet (in B♭ and A), Bassoon, Horn in F, Percussion (Timpani, Side Drum, Bass Drum, Cymbal, Gong), Harp, two Violins, Viola, Violoncello, Double Bass.

Duration : 85 minutes

*Note: The Boys' Choir is accompanied throughout by an organ, and it may be found advisable to use an harmonium or portable organ for this purpose since the sound should be distant. A grand organ (ad lib.) *plays with the orchestra in the last movement only.*

B. & H. 18940

WAR REQUIEM

Text from the "Missa pro Defunctis"
and the poems of Wilfred Owen*
*Deutsche Übertragung
von Dietrich Fischer-Dieskau
und Ludwig Landgraf*

BENJAMIN BRITTEN
Op. 66

1. REQUIEM AETERNAM

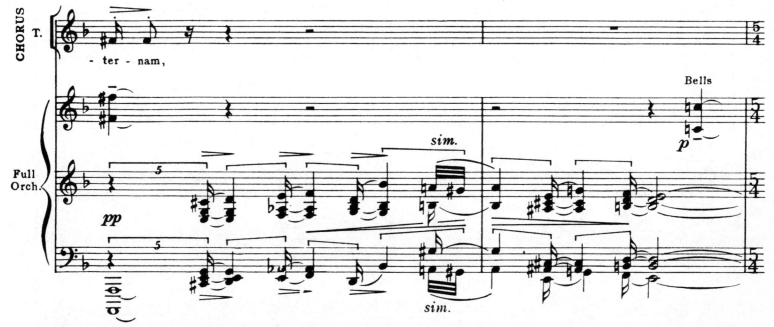

* The poems of Wilfred Owen are reprinted by permission of Mr. Harold Owen and Chatto & Windus Ltd.

© 1962 by Boosey & Hawkes Music Publishers Ltd.
German Translation © 1963 by Boosey & Hawkes Music Publishers Ltd.

B. & H. 18940

6

8

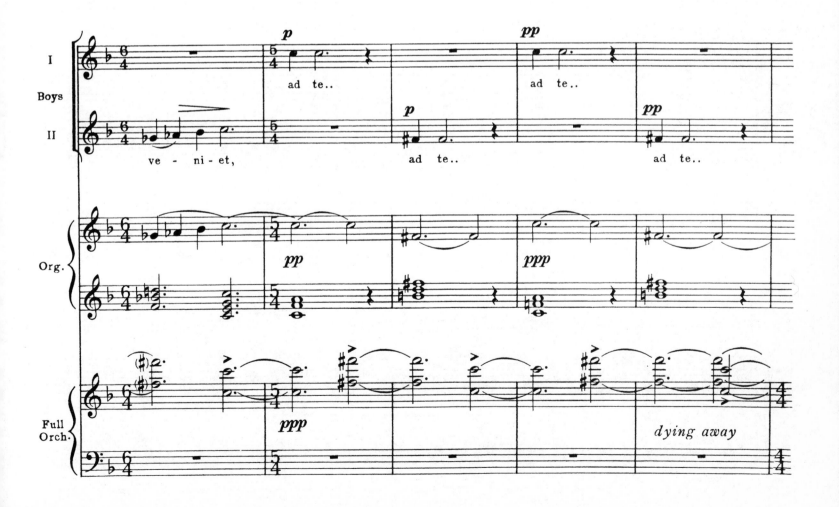

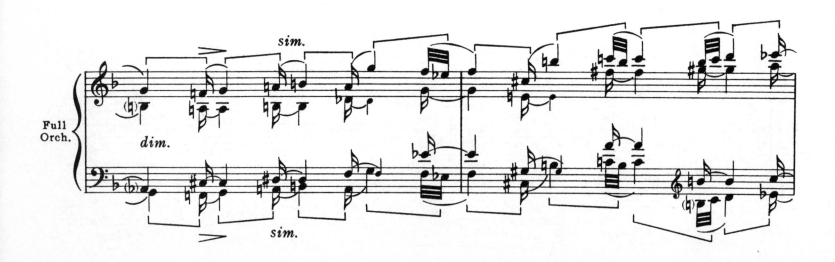

16

slowly relaxing
(*poco a poco rilassando*)

flo-wers the ten-der-ness of si-lent minds,
Blu - men - strauss die Zart-heit stil - ler Ruh'

And each slow
Und Däm - mer -

dusk a draw - ing- down of blinds.
- ung zieht dann den Vor - hang zu.

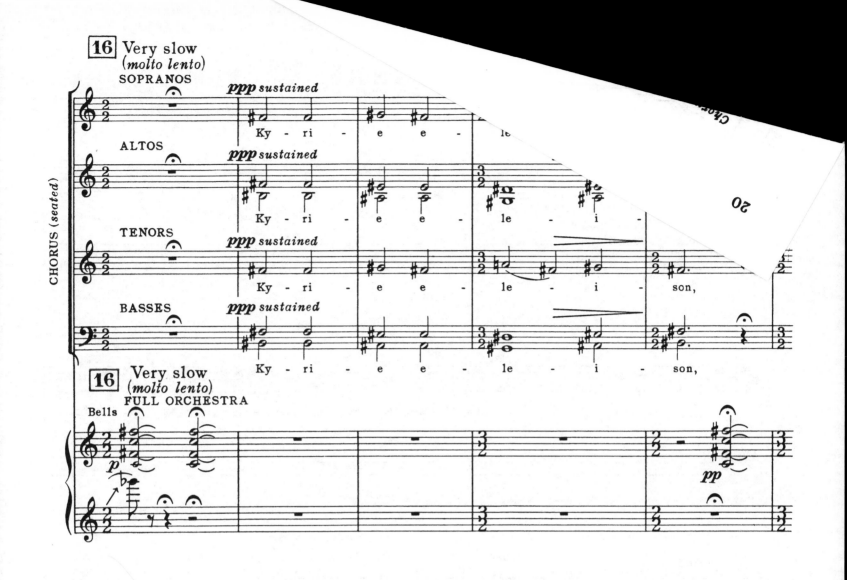

2. DIES IRAE

Cun-cta stri-cte dis-cus - su-rus!

Cun-cta stri-cte dis-cus - su-rus!

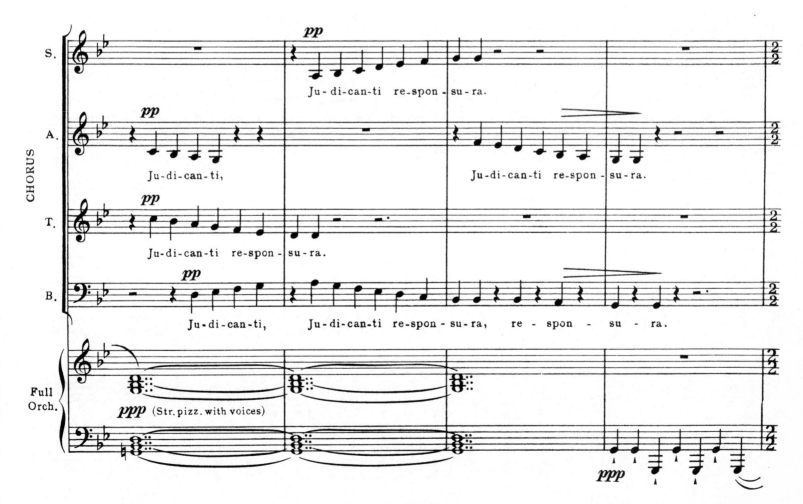

B. & H. 18940

B. & H. 18940

3. OFFERTORIUM

74

77

* If rehearsed with piano, this should be played as follows:

with Ped.

† Repeat this bar ad lib. until entry of Soloists and Chamber Orchestra is heard.

4. SANCTUS

B. & H. 18940

* chanting freely

* chanting freely

CHORUS

Full Orch.

* chanting freely

B. & H. 18940

122

B. & H. 18940

5. AGNUS DEI

And in their fa-ces there is pride That they were flesh-marked by the Beast By whom the gen - tle
Dem Stolz das Antlitz blass entstellt, Dass ihn der Be-stie Zei-chen traf, Die nicht zum mil - den

Christ's__ de - nied._____
Je - sus hält._____

A - gnus De-i, qui tol-lis pec - ca - ta mun - di, do - na e - is re-qui - em.

A - gnus De-i, qui tol-lis pec - ca - ta mun - di, do - na e - is re-qui - em.

A - gnus De-i, qui tol-lis pec - ca - ta mun - di, do - na e - is re-qui - em._____

98 FULL ORCHESTRA

B. & H. 18940

6. LIBERA ME

March starting slowly (♩ = approx. 63) with gradual accelerando until 116
(*Marcia*)

168

B. & H. 18940

(Brass with Chorus)

B. & H. 18940

Reproduced and printed by
Halstan & Co. Ltd., Amersham, Bucks., England

SELECTED CHORAL WORKS ON SALE

Works with orchestra/ensemble

Argento
I Hate and I Love
Te Deum
Toccata of Galuppi's

Bernstein
Chichester Psalms
Kaddish (Symphony No.3)
Missa Brevis

Britten
Ballad of Heroes
Cantata Academica
Cantata Misericordium
Saint Nicolas
Spring Symphony
War Requiem

Copland
Canticle of Freedom

Delius
Sea Drift

Einem
An die Nachgeborenen

Ferguson
Amore Langueo

Finzi
For St Cecilia
In Terra Pax
Intimations of Immortality
Lo, the Full, Final Sacrifice

Floyd
A Time to Dance

Ginastera
Turbae ad Passionem Gregorianam

Goldschmidt
Letzte Kapitel

Górecki
Salve, sidus Polonorum

Horne
Pensive

Ireland
These Things Shall Be

Kodály
Missa Brevis

MacMillan
Cantos Sagrados
Magnificat and Nunc Dimittis

Maw
The Ruin

Maxwell Davies
First Ferry to Hoy
The Shepherds' Calendar

Rorem
Little Prayers
Te Deum

Rouse
Karolju

Stravinsky
Cantata
Canticum Sacrum
Mass
Requiem Canticles
A Sermon, A Narrative and a Prayer
Symphony of Psalms
Threni

Works with organ
or other instrument as stated

Argento
Peter Quince at the Clavier
SATB and piano

Britten
A Ceremony of Carols
SSA/SATB and harp or piano
Rejoice in the Lamb

Finzi
Lo, the Full, Final Sacrifice
Magnificat

Horne
Magnificat and Nunc Dimittis
Pensive

Kodály
Laudes Organi
Missa Brevis

MacMillan
Cantos Sagrados
Magnificat and Nunc Dimittis
Mass
Te Deum

Maxwell Davies
Solstice of Light

Rorem
Miracles of Christmas
SATB and organ or piano

BOOSEY & HAWKES

Boosey & Hawkes Music Publishers Limited
www.boosey.com